Beautiful

sharing our faith with friends and neighbours

course member's booklet

Roger Morgan

ReSource

ReSource – helping to build a church which is diverse, local, renewed in the Spirit and effective in mission

Published by ReSource
13 Sadler Street, Wells, Somerset BA5 2RR
www.resource-arm.net
Charity no. 327035

ISBN 978-1-906363-29-1

Further information and support from ReSource

If you would like support from Roger Morgan or another member of the
ReSource team as you use this course, or if you would like to talk to us about
running outreach events or local missions, please do get in touch by email at
office@resource-arm.net or by phone on 01749 672865.

Additional resources to support your evangelism are available on our website:
Stay Evangelism (the booklet which accompanies this course), *Decision*
(probably the best short introduction to faith for new or potential Christians,
ideal for use with Alpha and outreach events) and the *Oikos* prayer cards
(designed to help you to pray for friends who are not yet Christians).

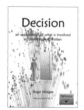

Beautiful Lives

A course to help ordinary Christian believers reach out to their friends and neighbours with the intention that some of these friends and neighbours will become believers too.

This course lasts for eight sessions. It is written for groups of between four and ten people. The course is contained in a leader's book, and each member of the course will need a copy of this course member's booklet.

The course includes the planning and preparation of an event which will take place some time after the course has been completed. This is an event to which course members will invite unchurched friends.

The homework contained in this member's booklet is designed to encourage and help you to adopt a lifestyle which is outreaching, deliberately loving, and evangelistic. Each week you will enter into your normal life with the determination to apply what you have learned on the course, and you will report back to the group at the end of the week. It is essential that each member of the group should enter wholeheartedly into this homework.

The course will not be effective unless every participant is fully committed to the group and is able to attend all eight sessions. Exceptions can be made to cover particularly difficult personal circumstances, but 100% attendance should be both the aim and the norm. This will ensure that you reap the full benefit of the course and that you are able as a group to work together on the special outreach event which will follow the course. If you do need to miss a session you should try and meet up with another member of the group who will help you to catch up.

You will need to take a Bible and this booklet to the sessions.

Contents

Beautiful Lives

'May they be won over without a word.. when they see the purity and reverence of your lives. Let your adornment be the inner self with the lasting beauty of a gentle and quiet spirit.' (1 Peter 3.24)

'Beauty is commonly trivialized in our culture, whether secular or ecclesial. It is reduced to decoration, equated with the insipidities of "pretty" or "nice." But beauty is not an add-on, not an extra, not a frill. Beauty is fundamental. Beauty is evidence of and witness to the inherent wholeness and goodness of who God is and the way God works. It is life in excess of what we can manage or control.' (Eugene Peterson, *The Jesus Way*, Hodder 2007)

'Beauty of life causes strangers to join our ranks. We do not talk about great things; we live them' (Minucius Felix, Rome, 160-240 AD)

Beautiful Lives Week 1
The growth of the Church in Acts

Course material for Week 1

The growth of the church following the resurrection – a study from the Book of Acts

- Acts 1.8 - Jesus tells his disciples that this will be his last physical appearance to them. Instead the Holy Spirit will come upon them and they will be his witnesses, first in Judea, which was where they were living, then in Samaria, which was the nearest place after that, and then to the world.

- Acts 2.1-4 - The Holy Spirit comes upon the disciples as Jesus had promised.

- Acts 2.22-24 - The disciples actively begin to witness as Jesus had told them to.

- Acts 2.41 - The 120 see 3000 people come to faith in Jesus on a single day.

- Acts 2.42-46 - The new community in Jerusalem which is filled by the Holy Spirit.

- Acts 2.47 - Others see this community in action and also become believers.

- Acts 6.7 - The Church grows even bigger.

- Acts 11.19-21 - The good news spreads to other cities including Antioch.

- Acts 13.1-5 - Paul and Barnabas are sent out by the Church in Antioch to take the gospel to the rest of the world.

Homework for Week 1

This week's homework is based on the story of the Good Samaritan in **Luke 10.25-37**. Read this story carefully on each day of the week so that you become very familiar with it. Each time you read it, pray for the people you met yesterday, and ask that God will fill you with his love as you prepare to meet new people on the day ahead. Enthusiasts may enjoy keeping a diary describing what happened each day. Whether you keep a diary or not, remember that you will have to report back to the group at the end of the week.

The difference between the Priest and the Levite and the Samaritan is seen in v 33. The Samaritan had pity on the injured man. So today your plan is to have pity for each person you meet.

The word 'pity' means 'sympathy'. The Samaritan saw the injured man as someone like himself - his own child perhaps, or a close friend. Today we plan to treat each person we meet as being a person of great importance - in fact someone as important to us as ourselves. We will do this by going through each day as slowly as possible so that we have time to notice the other people around us and to respond sympathetically to them.

The degree of involvement we can have with people will vary a great deal from person to person, but try to treat each person as being important to you, because each one is important to God.

This is where I would like you to begin to take this course very seriously and start living each day as you have probably never lived before. I want you to agree with me that it is time for you to get out of your comfort zone. People matter to God—let them matter to you more than they have ever mattered before. Give your absolute attention to each person that comes across your path this week. You will probably find this utterly exhausting, but you will also find it utterly absorbing.

Some people you will notice perhaps as you pass them in the street. You will look at their faces, wonder what life is like for them and pray for them. But there will be no opportunity for you to speak.

With other people you will have an opportunity to smile or to say something polite such as thank you or hello. It is important to do these little things well.

With other people it will be possible to stop and engage in conversation. This will usually be because it is someone you know, or it may be that it is easy to start a conversation (for example if you are at a party or next to someone in the Post Office queue). The purpose of this conversation is to encourage the other person and to send them on their way lifted by what you said to them.

With some people this conversation will turn into a heart-to-heart. You ask them how they are, and they share something of how life is for them; you listen and perhaps share what is going on for you.

In some cases you will find, as the Good Samaritan found, that there is something for you to do. There is some way for you to put yourself out to meet the need in the other person or at least offer to do so.

In some cases you will find yourself fixing an appointment to take the relationship further in some way.

As you go through each day look out for examples of each one of the above.

At the supermarket and in the office

These examples describe the experiences of some people who used this homework exercise.

Sue did her shopping at the supermarket. That day she was trying hard not to be in a hurry and to take in each person as she met them. She was able to smile at the checkout girl, to pray for her and to say thank you. The next time she shopped she noticed that the checkout girl was looking very tired. "Had a long shift today?" said Sue. "Yes, but I'll soon be home – you are my last one today." This brief island of caring was appreciated. Sue found on that one day that she was able to lift the lives of quite a number of people.

John left his office to walk to a meeting across the town. He made sure he had five minutes to spare so that he was not in a hurry. He passed lots of people, trying to take them in and pray for them. Suddenly someone stopped to ask him the way to a particular street. John did not know that street but he had a map in his office. So he took the stranger back to his office and was able to give him directions. John was still in time for his meeting.

Arthur went to his work in a large office building. That day began with a meeting with Bill; Bill worked in the same building but Arthur had not met him before. The subject of the meeting was quite technical and their business lasted an hour and a half. But Arthur had been praying for Bill throughout this time and had tried to serve Bill's interests in the meeting. When the meeting was over Arthur and Bill walked down the corridor together. Arthur offered, "It's been good meeting you this morning – do you have time to meet up for lunch one day?" Bill was glad to accept.

"Let your light so shine before men that they may see your good works and glorify your Father who is in heaven" - Matthew 5.16

Beautiful Lives Week 2
Go evangelism and Stay evangelism

Course material for Week 2

A prayer in which we ask God to give us his Holy Spirit

"Lord Jesus, thank you for the gift of life you have given me.
From today I commit myself to making a new start. I am
sometimes tempted to trust in myself or in other things,
but I promise that from today I will try to trust you for all
the big issues in my life. I know I have not always lived as I
should, and sometimes I get my priorities all wrong. I want to become
the person you made me to be. I want to turn away from anything that
is wrong, and today I promise to try to make you the most important
thing in my life.

"I commit myself today to love and serve you by giving time to developing
my relationship with you, and by the way I live among other people.
Please Lord fill me with your Holy Spirit, so that I may display your
presence by the way that I live. May your love flow from me to every person
I meet. May my heart shine because it is filled with your joy and your peace.
May I be gentle, patient, kind and good. May I learn faithfulness, reliability
and self-control, so that my choices are Christ-like. In Jesus' name, Amen."

Homework for Week 2

How did you get on with last week's homework? Did you make every
effort? Did you discipline yourself to take in lots and lots of people? Did
you find that you had compassion for them? Did these people start to
matter to you? Are you beginning to weep for them in the drabness of
their lives? Have you begun to see that God is already at work in ways
that have surprised you?

Well, if you didn't, it is not too late, because the homework this week is very similar to the homework for last week. Please go out into your normal daily lives and try to live beautifully. Go slowly through life, notice people, stop for them when you can. Speak with them when you can. Always be careful to listen. And help people whenever you have the opportunity.

If you tried really hard to do this last week you probably found that at times you became quite weary, and that it was very tempting to give up and go back to a more self centred lifestyle. So this week we are going to try and avoid that by learning the truth contained in **Matthew 11.28-30**. Anyone who truly tries to live for others knows that this does not work unless we learn how to come to Jesus and find his refreshment. It is as if we are given the Holy Spirit, but then the Holy Spirit leaks out from us and we are empty again. This week we will not relent from our purpose to live for others, but at the same time we will learn the secret of being refilled again and again.

Look at **Mark 1.32-35**. That day, right up to bedtime, Jesus was busy living for others to a point where he probably felt overwhelmed by all the people. The next day we find him up early to pray seeking refreshment from his Father in heaven. Our secret will be to do the same.

So find somewhere solitary to pray (i.e. somewhere where you cannot be disturbed) and go there as early in the day as possible. Plan to stick to this place and this time throughout this week. Decide in advance how long you will stay in your solitary place with God. Half an hour is usually good but some will find fifteen minutes long enough at first, and others may need an hour or more.

How will you fill this prayer time? Well it's up to you – if you already have a really good system, stick to it. But in case you haven't here is a suggestion:

Begin by setting your mind on heaven, where Jesus is seated at the right hand of God. A good way to do this is to meditate through chapters 4 and 5 of Revelation. These chapters present a vision of heaven. Read very slowly and prayerfully, and you will find yourself beginning to visualise John's picture of heaven. On the first day start at the beginning of chapter 4 and read just a few verses, imagining yourself present in heaven and looking with wonder at the amazing scene. Ask the Holy Spirit to come and help you to do this.

The next day begin at the beginning again. This time go a bit further in the passage, until at the end of the week you are able perhaps to reach into chapter 5. What you are doing in this exercise is coming out of yourself and into God. He is the centre. He is the greater reality. When you go out again into the world you need to take a little bit of heaven with you.

Part of a team

Robert worked in an office and was made the leader of a new project team. Robert was excited about the project, but realised that the team had been given a tough assignment. What happened in practice was that relationships within the team began to deteriorate – no big rows but a lot of small niggles. Robert feared that the project would fail unless the team began to trust each other and work together. Robert brought this to God in prayer and God showed him that unless he himself changed he could not expect the others to change. So one day Robert got up early to pray. He spent an hour with God in his bedroom and then continued his prayer and meditation throughout his journey to work. As he entered the office that day his mind and his heart were full of how much God loved him. He found that his heart was full of love for the people in his team and he discovered a new ability to listen to them patiently. Everything changed from that day. Robert continued with his daily prayer times. The team came together and the project was a success. Much later people from that team accepted Robert's invitation to join an Alpha course at his church.

Next use the prayer asking for the Holy Spirit which you prayed in the group - you will find it at the beginning of this week's homework. Each day pray it again slowly and carefully asking Jesus to be the Lord of your life today and to live in you and through you. Then be quiet and listen and ask Jesus to speak to you. Write down anything he says.

Finally read a Psalm. Begin this week with Psalm 91 and go on to Psalm 97 by the end of the week. Read the Psalm slowly and with great attention. Now pray for the day ahead and then go out and live it for Jesus.

New neighbours

Charles and Katie moved into the empty house across the road from us in Leicester. We prayed for them and waited for an opportunity. One day as I was coming out of my house I noticed that Charles was standing at his garden gate. I went straight across the road and welcomed him. Charles was obviously very pleased and we were soon engaged in an enjoyable conversation. I asked if Charles and Katie would care to have dinner with us and they accepted. We became good friends and it was easy for us to tell Charles and Katie our story of faith because they were keen to hear about it. Things went on from there – when they moved in Charles and Katie were not Christians but now they are very much part of the Church and we have become life long friends.

Learning from history

The greatest expansion of the gospel took place in the second and third centuries. An observation made in the year 150 AD explains why: 'Beauty of life causes strangers to join our ranks. We do not talk about great things; we live them.'

Beautiful Lives Week 3
Who are our friends and neighbours?

Homework for Week 3

Continue with the lifestyle that you tried to adopt in the previous two weeks. Begin each day with prayer. Ask the Holy Spirit to take you over. Go as slowly as you can through the days. Notice people. Pray for them. Talk to them. Help them if you can.

In your prayer times use any methods that work for you. Perhaps you will wish to carry on with what you did last week. But you may find that it helps to have some new ideas, and if so you might like to try the following:

Some days it can be hard to pray because there is something that is bothering you. Maybe it is something that went wrong, or some way in which you were hurt, or something in the days ahead that you are anxious about. **Colossians 2.7** tells us to abound in thankfulness, but this is hard to do when things are going wrong. So begin your prayer time by making a list of all the things that went right on the previous day. Don't stop until you have a list of six things – there really always are six! Then beneath your list write down the one thing that has gone wrong. Now pray through all seven items thanking God for each one – including the seventh.

Another idea is to meditate each day on **Psalm 23**. Concentrate on one of the following thoughts from the psalm. You might also find it helpful to draw a picture to go with each thought – any kind of picture you like so long as it captures what the psalm is saying.

1. The Lord is my shepherd. Today he will make me lie down in green pastures. That is the kind of God he is and the kind of relationship he has with me.

2. The Lord is my shepherd. Today he will lead me beside still waters and will restore my soul.

3. The Lord is my shepherd. For his sake today he will lead me in right paths.

4. The Lord is my shepherd. Even if today I walk through the darkest valley I will fear no evil. For he will be with me; his rod and his staff will comfort me.

5. The Lord is my shepherd. Today he will prepare a table for me in the presence of my enemies.

6. The Lord is my shepherd. Today he will anoint my head with oil and my cup will overflow.

7. The Lord is my shepherd. Today I shall dwell in his house. Today I will know his goodness and his mercy.

Each day use one of these seven thoughts. Begin by relating the thought to your past life. For example if the thought you are using today is the last one, thought 7, get back in touch with the time when you knew for sure that God was your shepherd, when you dwelt in his house, and knew his goodness and mercy.

Then each day bring the thought into the present and realise that today the Lord is still your shepherd, today you will enjoy living in his house and experiencing his goodness and mercy.

Last week at the group you made a list of names. Some of the names were people you know very well (you gave them at least five ticks in the exercise). Make sure you pray for these people every day, asking that one day soon they will hear the word of God and respond to it.

You also listed some people (at least two) who you don't know quite so well but who you decided you would take steps to get to know better. Take these steps this week. Maybe you should go and visit them or send a text or make a phone call. Maybe you should suggest something that you could do together. Maybe you could give them an invitation to come for a meal at your house, or just a coffee.

A lost opportunity

I once heard Billy Graham, the great American evangelist, speak about two people who had worked together for years. One of them – let's call him John – became a Christian at one of Billy's meetings. He went to work the next day and told his friend Tom all about it. "How splendid," said Tom, "now we are not only partners at work but brothers in the Lord." "What," said John, "you are a Christian?" "Yes" said Tom, "for many years." John was very angry. "For years I have worked with you and admired the way you live. You are the main reason why I have not sought after God. I figured that if someone could live as well as you do without God, then God wasn't necessary. Why didn't you tell me?" Tom realised that he had had many opportunities to share his faith with John but he had never done so.

Dave's story

After six years in Corby I went to Leicester, where I was immediately impressed by Dave, a keen young Christian who had a secular job as a computer expert with a brewery chain. Dave approached me, offering himself as a full time go evangelist. I agreed with his priorities and respected his willingness but I was not sure that he was called to this. I suggested that until God spoke more clearly he should stay where he was and live as a stay evangelist.

Dave's job takes him far and wide. Recently he found himself attending a conference in Greece where he met Alexi, a Russian from Moscow, also a computer expert. Dave was reading his Bible in the hotel; Alexi approached him and asked Dave to explain the Bible to him. Dave opened the scriptures and shared the gospel. Alexi became a Christian and now attends a church in Moscow. Dave and I later had the pleasure of baptising him at our church in Leicester. I share this story because I believe this is how God normally works – through the lives of ordinary Christians like Dave who witness to people in the context of their daily secular life.

Beautiful Lives Week 4
Telling our story

Homework for Week 4

Please keep going with your daily life of prayer and your daily life of noticing and serving the people around you.

You can probably see by now what this course is all about. We are trying to show you that evangelism is not primarily about preaching on street corners or knocking on people's doors. In fact it is not primarily about speaking at all. It is primarily about living a beautiful life. If you understand this and do it consistently, you will find that not everyone but some people will become very interested in knowing what makes you tick.

When someone who is not a Christian first asks me about my faith I know that we have reached a critical moment. Will I say something sensible or will I fluff my lines? What I have learned from experience is that it is important to be ready to tell the story of how Jesus became the centre of my life.

The main homework this week is to write out the story of your own spiritual journey. It doesn't need to be long – about 300 words will be ideal. Don't skip this exercise. Do it thoroughly. You will never regret having a worked-out testimony and you will use it on many occasions.

When you have written out your story, find two friends, one a Christian and one not a Christian, and share your story with each of them in turn. Explain to each of them that you are attending a course at your church and have been asked to write out the story of your spiritual journey and then to check it out with two friends to see if it makes sense to them. Explain that you would like them to listen, and tell you afterwards whether the story makes sense and how they think it comes across. Does it ring true, is it interesting? Is it too long, or too boring? How do they respond to it?

In preparing your story first decide if you are more like Paul (Acts 26) or like Timothy (2 Timothy 1.3-6). In his early life Paul was definitely not a Christian, then a series of events occurred by which he became a Christian, and as a result his life changed completely. Timothy, on the other hand, learned his faith as a child and never gave up on it. Many Christians are like Paul and even more are like Timothy. But which are you?

More like Paul?

If you are more like Paul then write your story in three parts allowing 100 words for each part.

1. A description of your life before conversion (as Paul did in Acts 26.2-11)

2. The detailed story of your conversion (see Acts 26.12-18)

3. A description of your life since conversion (see Acts 26.19-23)

To help you do this, this first think out what has changed in your life as a result of your becoming a Christian. For example perhaps before conversion you believed in God but had no relationship with him, whereas afterwards you found that you had a relationship with God which worked. If this is the biggest change brought about by your conversion, use part 1 to describe what it was like to live with a faith that did not really work, and use part 3 to describe what life became like once you had a faith which did work.

Or maybe the biggest change that occurred for you was a moral one. Maybe before you were a Christian you lived a life of which you are now ashamed. In this case use part one of your story to describe life as it was and part three to describe life as it is now.

In the middle part just tell the story as a blow-by-blow account of the events which led to your conversion and how that actually happened. Was it as a result of saying a prayer, or was it a gradual process – what happened?

When you have written your 300 words, challenge yourself along the following lines. First of all does your story contain any jargon, i.e. words which would either be not understood by non Christians or jar with them? Secondly, is it interesting? If your story is really a story it will be interesting – if it is just a set of statements then it will not be interesting. Thirdly, is it clear – would somebody listening to it understand what is involved in becoming a Christian? Fourthly does it honour Jesus – is it the story of something that he did or just something that happened to you?

More like Timothy?

If you are more like Timothy then again write your story in three parts allowing 100 words for each part.

1. Childhood memories of faith

2. The story of your calling to serve the Lord (see 2 Timothy 1.6)

3. Adult outworkings of this calling

The most difficult part for you to write will probably be the middle one. First make a list of the key principles which are driving your life now, and the key purposes which are filling your heart and mind. Once this is done, ask yourself what has happened in your relationship with God which has led you to these principles and purposes. It is that story which will constitute part 2. Try to write a blow-by-blow account of crucial events in your life which led you to the convictions which you now live by. Part 3 will describe how those things are being worked out in your life right now. Part 1 will describewhat it was like to be brought up in a Christian home. Include some things that happened which showed that Jesus was alive and real in your home.

When you have finished writing, challenge yourself. Is what you have written free of jargon? Is it interesting? Clear? Does it honour Jesus? Now that you have written your story go and find two friends to share it with.

Now please think ahead. It is really important that you fit this part of the homework in. In two weeks' time, during week six of the course, we will receive some training on how to hold a conversation on a one-to-one basis or a couple to couple basis. So please plan ahead and set up some conversations for two weeks from now. For example invite a non-Christian friend round for a meal or make an arrangement to go out with someone or play a game with them or go for a walk. In the work context it may be possible to use lunch times or to see someone after work. Just try to make sure that in two weeks time you are not so busy that you do not have time to talk to anybody!

At the chess club

When I lived in Corby I joined the Corby chess club and played in matches in the Northampton league. I was glad to get to know my team mates, and we would often travel together to matches. The conversation was largely about chess. I tried my best to take a genuine interest in their games and not just talk about my own. But one evening one of the team asked me "Why is someone like you a vicar in Corby?" He had become interested in me, and this was my opportunity. I shared my testimony, which took me about 3 minutes. At the end I said, as I always do, "Does that make sense to you?" He was full of questions, and we arranged to meet and talk. It was not long before he was attending our church.

Beautiful Lives Week 5
How we live

Course material for Week 5

Questions about our integrity as Christians

1. Are you able to forgive others no matter how they have hurt you?
2. Are you able to promote others and not yourself?
3. Are you able to aim for peace with all people?
4. Are you always honest?
5. Are you able to keep your temper?
6. Is your speech honouring of others, or are you critical of them when they are absent?
7. Are you being faithful in your marriage in both your actions and your thoughts?
8. Do you always remain sober?
9. Do you live simply or extravagantly?
10. Are you free from anxiety or do you worry a lot?
11. Do you always keep your word?
12. Are you always on time for appointments?
13. Do you meet disappointment or misfortune with faith and cheerfulness?

Homework for Week 5

At the group this week we looked at various ways in which we can live beautiful lives. This week for homework use your daily prayer time to reinforce what you learned in the group time.

Meditating on Scripture

We saw that beautiful lives are a fruit of the Spirit's presence in our lives. One way in which the Holy Spirit works is to take the truths of scripture and impress these on our minds. So begin your prayer time this week by meditating on one or more of the following verses. All of these verses speak of the relationship between ourselves and God.

Romans 5.1	Galatians 2.20	Colossians 1.13
Romans 8.1	Ephesians 1.3	Colossians 1.14
1 Corinthians 1.30	Ephesians 1.4	Colossians 1.27
1 Corinthians 2.12	Ephesians 1.7-8	Colossians 2.7
1 Corinthians 3.18	Ephesians 1.12-14	Colossians 3.1-4
1 Corinthians 6.19-20	Ephesians 2.5	Hebrews 4.16
2 Corinthians 1.21	Ephesians 2.6	2 Peter 1.4
2 Corinthians 5.14-15	Ephesians 2.11	
2 Corinthians 5.21	Ephesians 3.12	

Wholeheartedness

When you have meditated on one or more of these verses each day, continue your prayer time by making a list of all the tasks that you know have to be done today. Look again at **Colossians 3.23** and make your mind up to have the attitude of the slave who will do his or her best at each of these tasks, so that at the end of the day they can be offered up to God for his approval. Each day look at yesterday's list and feel God's pleasure at the way you did things. Keep a diary if you have time.

Integrity

At the group we considered the following list of ways in which Jesus is asking us to live as his disciples:

1. Forgiving people no matter what how they have hurt us
2. Promoting others and not ourselves
3. Aiming for peace with all people whenever possible
4. Being completely honest
5. Keeping our tempers under control
6. Keeping our speech honouring to others, and not being critical of them when they are absent
7. Being faithful in our marriages, including keeping our thoughts under control
8. Always remaining sober
9. Living simply and not extravagantly
10. Keeping free from anxiety
11. Always keeping our word
12. Always being on time for appointments
13. Meeting disappointment or misfortune with faith and cheerfulness

At the group you were asked to choose one of these which you would particularly like to grow in. In your prayer time bring this area up every day and pray that God will give you his grace to live as you know you want to.

Prayer of Commitment

Use this prayer again as you did before:

"Lord Jesus, thank you for the gift of life you have given me. From today I commit myself to making a new start. I am sometimes tempted to trust in myself or in other things, but I promise that from today I will try to trust you for all the big issues in my life. I know that I have not always lived as I should, and someteims Iget my priorities all wrong. I want to become the person you made me to be. I want to turn away from anyting that is wrong, and today I promise to try to make you the most important thing in my life.

"I commit myself today to love and serve you by giving time to developing my relationship with you, and by the way I live among other people. Please Lord fill me with your Holy Spirit, so that I may display your presence by the way that I live. May your love flow from me to every person I meet. May my heart shine because it is filled with your joy and your peace. May I be gentle, patient, kind and good. May I learn faithfulness, reliability and self-control, so that my choices are Christ-like. In Jesus' name, Amen."

Setting up conversations

Next week at the course we will be learning how to hold conversations with people and the homework next week will involve us spending as much time as possible in one on one conversations with non Christians. So please do what you can to set this up in advance.

A dinner invitation

Sally had become a Christian. So had her three children. We knew her husband Ivor, but not well, and there had been no conversation with him beyond the superficial.

So we invited Sally and Ivor to dinner. We also invited Jill who had never met either of them. We trusted Jill because we knew she had a clear faith but would not try to push it on Ivor.

The evening was a great success as a social occasion. The five of us relaxed together and talked about many things including some personal issues. The subject of Christianity never came up — not raised by us, not raised by Ivor either. But we knew when Sally and Ivor left that we would always be good friends, and so it proved.

We also noticed that after that Ivor would be there sometimes on Sunday with Sally. About two years later Ivor asked if he could do the Alpha course and became a Christian.

Giving your best

In Cambridge it was part of my job to teach probability theory. Students came to see me in pairs. One pair came each week from Jesus College; they were bright and industrious, and I enjoyed the sessions. I worked hard trying to teach them to the best of my ability. I lived near Jesus College, and after one of the sessions, one of them helped me carry some equipment to my home. As we walked along, he opened the conversation. "They tell me you are a Christian," he said. "Yes," I said, "how about you?". "No," he said, "I am not, but I have been thinking about it a lot." "Would you know how to become a Christian if you wanted to?" "No," he said, "but could you explain?" So I gave him an outline of the gospel:

- A for *Admit* that you need something more.
- B for *Believe* and trust in Jesus.
- C for *Consider* what being a Christian will mean in practice.
- D for *Do*; offer up your life and receive the gift of the Holy Spirit.

Our walk across Cambridge lasted for about 10 minutes. Later that evening he prayed a prayer which I had given him, in the company of his friends back at the college.

Why had he chosen to speak to me? Not just because I am a Christian; there are many Christians in Cambridge. I think he spoke to me because of the way I had taught him probability theory.

A reluctant juror

A couple of years ago I was called for Jury service. At first this seemed like a major irritation, but God showed me that it was an opportunity – an opportunity to be wholehearted for the sake of being wholehearted. I really enjoyed it and really did my best to concentrate on the evidence and make my contribution to the jury. I got my reward at the end when one of the other jurors said to me "The thing about you Roger, is that you are all heart." It was not difficult to take my opportunity and tell him why.

Beautiful Lives Week 6
Getting into conversation

Course material for **Week 6**

Planning an event for our friends

Would your particular friends feel comfortable if

1. They knew they **were coming** to a discussion?
2. They knew they **were coming** to enjoy a good meal?
3. They were coming **to share in** some kind of outing?
4. They knew that **they would be** listening to a good speaker?
5. They knew that **they would be** playing a game of some sort?
6. They knew that **they would be** listening to people telling their stories?
7. They knew that if **they wanted** to someone would pray for them in confidence?
8. They knew that **there would be** background music?
9. They knew that **there would be** singing of religious songs?

Which of the following **topics would** be interesting to your friends?

1. Stress – causes, **symptoms** and cures, and where faith fits in
2. Money, sex and **power – good** for us or bad for us?
3. How to be happy
4. Has Science made God unnecessary?
5. When things go **wrong** - strategies for coping in life's most difficult moments
6. How to deal with **difficult people**
7. How to live a life that makes a difference

Homework for Week 6

The main task this week is to create opportunities for one-on-one (or couple to couple) conversations with unchurched people.

In the course of each day you probably have many brief conversations with all sorts of people. Your aim in these brief conversations is to encourage people, to lighten their load and lift their spirits. The home-work this week is not about these brief conversations but about much longer ones, from 15 to 60 minutes in duration. Conversations of this length are an essential part of getting to know someone and coming closer to them. Such conversations sometimes happen without being planned, but they are much more likely to happen if you think ahead.

Titus 1.8 makes being hospitable a qualification for anyone who wants to be a church leader. **Romans 12.13** says that all Christians should be hospitable to strangers. Being hospitable may mean offering someone a bed for the night, inviting someone home for a meal, or taking someone to a pub for a drink. Hospitality is a normal part of being a Christian. But hospitality also always provides us with an excellent opportunity for conversation.

Conversations can arise in other ways, especially if we travel around a lot by public transport. If you are on a plane or a train, try opening up a conversation with those around you, and you will be amazed by how high a proportion of people will welcome the chance to talk.

However your conversations arise, the wise approach is not to talk about yourself or air your own opinions, but rather to take a genuine interest in the other person.

Some people will reciprocate very quickly and take an interest in you in return. If and when they do, then talk about yourself, your ideas and your feelings about life. You will find that it is often possible to talk about your faith and the story of how you became a Christian.

If you take an interest in someone and they just go on talking about themselves don't worry about this. The fact is they probably need to talk, and it may be that other people rarely listen to them. It may take a long time but eventually you will probably find that they do start to ask questions.

Remember the plan for a conversation which we discussed in the group session. Unless you know someone quite well, always begin at the factual level. Ask questions which show a genuine interest in learning facts about the other person. Make connections whenever you can – if you discovered that he loves football and you also love football, then talk about football.

As the conversation proceeds at this factual level, ask yourself how you

The power of neighbourliness

I heard this story from one of my fellow clergy who became the vicar of a rural parish. After he went to work there the church began to grow. New people came to church and some of them became Christians. He then realised that all of the new people lived close to one another. Further investigation revealed that all the new people had started to come to church because of one family. He then tried to discover why, and came to the conclusion that all the family were doing was being extremely good neighbours. They had got to know their neighbours, been hospitable to them and made themselves available to help at every opportunity. This key family had never tried to push their Christianity on anyone; but the neighbours, observing that the family went to church, decided one by one that they would try it too.

could develop it into a discussion. Is there some issue about which you would like to know your friend's opinions? Once you know what he or she thinks on this issue, then you can share your own thoughts, and this should lead into a discussion.

The third stage of a conversation comes when you move on from facts and opinions to feelings. Even as you are talking, you should be thinking all the time about how this person feels about their life. Then find a way to ask them. One thing that often works is to ask people how they feel about the future. Ask "What would you ideally like to be doing in ten years' time?"

As your friend shares, listen very carefully, and try to empathise and understand. Sometimes it happens that you have had a very similar experience and if so it will probably help if you share this. But don't claim to know how your friend feels if you have never felt like that yourself.

All conversations have to end. But before you end the conversation think of a way in which you can continue the relationship. Perhaps you have talked and laughed about football. Why not suggest to your friend that you go to a game together?

Remember that in all this there is one very important principle. We may want all our friends to become Christians, but we don't make friends just for that reason. We make friends for the genuine reason that we want to be friends, and if in the end this person never becomes a believer, make up your mind to stay friends.

Getting it wrong

Years ago, when I was working in Cambridge, I had a colleague called Mike. Mike and I had a good working relationship, but I had not made any effort to make friends with him. I did invite him to things at my church, but he never accepted the invitations. It wasn't surprising really – people accept invitations from friends, people they feel they trust because they know them.

Mike and I had the same boss. I didn't like my boss and, as it turned out, neither did Mike. One day we were told by the boss that Mike was leaving to take a job in another university on the south coast. I assumed that Mike had got a promotion. Mike left and I guess I thought I would never see him again.

Some years after that my wife and I spent a holiday week in a hotel in Majorca. As it happened, staying in the same hotel were Mike and his wife. We asked them to join us for coffee and tried to make friends with them. (You ask me why I hadn't done this before in Cambridge and I am without excuse!) In Majorca we learned the truth about Mike's relationship with our former boss. I'd had a hard time with him but for Mike it had been much worse and much more unfair. Mike had been forced out of the department and had been glad to find a job anywhere. But it had been bad for his family and they had never recovered properly from it. We listened carefully to their story and were able to sympathise. After an hour of listening and talking about Cambridge and their family they turned the subject to us and what we were doing. The last hour of the evening consisted of a serious and open conversation about the Christian faith. How I wish I had had this conversation years before in Cambridge!

Beautiful Lives Week 7
Speaking and loving

Homework for Week 7

Becoming the Word of God to other people

Jesus is the incarnate word. Everything about him communicated a message from God, a message which had great impact on the world. At the group meeting we saw how today we Christians, filled by the Holy Spirit as Jesus was, are called to be the Word of God today to other people. Everything we do and say – the whole of our life – is meant to deliver a message to the people we meet.

Here are three ways in which you can deliver this message. Each day this week, do your best to do these things and at the end of each day review how this went.

1. Go slowly, notice everybody, do whatever you can to lift their lives.

2. Perform each task that is put in front of you to the best of your ability as if you were doing each task entirely to please God.

3. Make all the difficult choices that you face with integrity being determined to follow the principles that Jesus taught. Promote others. Forgive others. Be truthful. Be faithful. Keep your word.

Connecting with people

Try this week to go out of your way to make contact with each of the people on your short list of contacts. You could phone, send an email or a text, or just go round to see them. You could invite them for a meal, suggest an outing, or just exchange news but whatever you do spend a bit of time with each one of them. It is the purpose of God to make friends with each of your friends and the way he does this initially is through you.

Praying for your friends

In the group this week we saw how important is the life of our Christian community in spreading the Word of God. Evangelism is something that we do together. Make a list of the people who belong to the group with which you are doing this course. Every day in your prayer time lift at least two of these people before the Lord. Ask him to speak to you about them and to show you how you can love them. If you know their needs, ask God to meet their needs. If you have time make a call later that day to see how they are each doing.

Praying for yourself

Finally, in your prayer time as well as doing some of the prayer exercises learned from previous weeks pray the following prayer:

"Lord, today speak through my words, my actions, my smile, my helpfulness. Lord, today may I be wholehearted in the way I do every task and may this speak to those who work with me.

The importance of integrity

The people in our family and friendship groups are watching us. My neighbour Aidan, not yet a Christian, has become very much part of our church community and knows the men of his own age very well. He told me that he does not respect their integrity. "The reason I do not become a Christian," he said, "is because I have read the Sermon on the Mount and I do not wish to live by it – it's too hard for me. But I meet a lot of Christians who do not live by it either." I reflected that until our church changes the way it lives it will not convince Aidan.

Lord, today may I be friendly to everyone I meet. Show me today a way to turn my acquaintances into friends.

Lord, today may I have an opportunity to listen to somebody else's heartbeat.

Lord, today may I have an opportunity to make a sacrifice for someone.

Lord, today may I be welcoming as others come to my home or to my workplace.

Lord, today may I have an opportunity to tell someone my story.

Two businessmen

Keith and Alan were businessmen with important, high pressure jobs. But they were also Christians, and anxious to live in a way that reflected Jesus to others. They decided to spend a day going more slowly and trying to be more aware of people.

Keith went to work that day and parked his car at his workplace. As he left he car park, he noticed the attendant. "Lord Jesus," he prayed, "what do I say to a man I have ignored for 3 years?" The man's name was on his uniform. "Good morning, Charlie," Keith said. "Good morning, Mr Miller" - so Charlie knew his name. "Charlie, do you have a family?". Charlie pulled out a picture of his six children. A friendship began that day between Keith and Charlie, and later that year Keith was able to visit one of those children in hospital. Keith found to his amazement that his office had lots of Charlies, people he had never really taken in before.

Alan went to work by train. Late as usual, he ran down the station steps, turned the corner and bumped into a small boy carrying a jigsaw. The pieces went everywhere, and Alan saw that he had a choice. Watching his train pull away from the platform, Alan helped the boy pick up the pieces. When they had finished the boy looked at Alan. "Mr," he said, "are you Jesus?". Alan realised that for five minutes, perhaps for the first time in his life, he had indeed been Jesus.

Stories from *A Second Touch*, Keith Miller, World Books 1967.

Beautiful Lives Week 8
Listening to the Holy Spirit

Taking life slowly

This week as you go through each day take life as
slowly as possible. Try to notice each person who
comes into your life. This is an exercise we have
done many times, but this time think of every
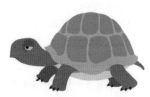
encounter as being like a triangle – you, the other person, and the Holy
Spirit. This is an exercise in multi-tasking and not everyone is good at this!
But have a try. Take in the other person but at the same time listen to the
Holy Spirit. Ask "What do you want me to say, Lord? and "What do you
want me to do, Lord?" and "What is going on here, Lord?" Always act or
speak on the basis of what you think the Lord may be saying to you or
indicating to you. You will soon learn how to sort out the difference between what is coming from the Holy Spirit and what is the product of
your own imagination.

Taking prayer seriously

The ability that Jesus had to work in this way was developed
in the extended prayer times he had alone with his Father.
It is very easy to let our prayer times slip, and it is very easy
to let them become no more than a routine. If this has been
happening, remember that you are human and that this is
normal. And make a decision to start again.

Get up early and find a place of solitude. Thirty minutes is ideal – longer
for some. This week begin your prayer time by reading a passage of
scripture. Try **Mark 1.1-13**, and then the next day choose another chunk
of Mark – again about ten verses. Before you begin reading, ask the Holy
Sprit to speak to you, and then read the passage very slowly chewing
over each word. As he speaks to you, respond to him.

Then pray for at least two of the members of the group with whom you are doing this course, and for each of the people who you are hoping to invite to the event that is being planned.

Finally make a list of all the things that you have planned for today and all the people who you expect to meet. Pray through this list and as you do so ask God to speak to you about each item and each person. If you think God may be speaking to you, try to follow his guidance.

Praying for those we meet

This week at the group we prayed for some of the needs that were revealed among the group members. This exercise will extend that – instead of praying for our Christian friends, which we are probably used to doing, we will try to learn to pray for the specific needs of everyone we meet.

As you go through your days you should be becoming aware of one person after another. With some of these people your encounter will be very brief and you will have no idea what their deeper needs are. Praying for them is no more than praying "Lord bless this person". But in other cases you will become aware of the other person's needs, especially if you are listening to the Holy Spirit as well as to the person themselves.

Often the needs are ones which you yourself can help with (as in the Good Samaritan story), but sometimes the person has needs that you cannot meet. This is when it is good to offer to pray for them. Ask the Holy Spirit what to say, and realise that in some cases it is best to say nothing. But there are occasions when it is possible gently to ask someone, "Is this something we could pray about?" or sometimes just to ask the other person if they have a faith of any kind. If they say that they do, you could then ask "Would you like us to pray about it?" If the other person does welcome prayer do it straight away, even if you are out in the street. You will be surprised how often such prayers get an immediate answer. What is more, it will make a deep impression that you have a faith in God in which you expect him to do things for you.

Servant or child?

Richard was involved in a Mission to Newcastle. During the Mission he was entertained to lunch by a lady called Gladys. The food was good, but in conversation Gladys was very down on herself and showed that she considered herself to be a bad person. Richard listened but did not know what to say, so he decided to talk to God about it there and then. He uttered a silent prayer: "Lord, this is a very nice lady who is consumed by her guilt. Please show me how to help her." As he prayed, an idea came to his mind.

"Mrs Robson, would you mind if I asked you a question?"
"Fire away" she said.
"Would you say that you are a child of God or a servant of God?"– this was the idea Richard had had, one he had never used before.
"I am a servant of God" she said, "but what is the difference between a servant of God and a child of God?"

Richard asked her if she had ever been a servant.
"Yes I have, I have worked for many people."
"What happened when you did a bad job?"
"I got the sack."

Gladys revealed that she had indeed got the sack on a couple of occasions, and clearly she felt that she had deserved it. Then Richard asked her "Do you have any children?" Gladys had five children.
"What happened when your children behaved badly?"
"I loved them even more," said Gladys.
It turned out that one of her children was a black sheep but that he still had a big place in her heart.

"So is it better to be a servant or a child?" asked Richard.

"A child," said Gladys. Richard took Gladys to John 1.12 and showed her how to become a child of God. They prayed together. Gladys became a child of God and her life completely changed.

The biggest order

Douglas is a Christian. One day in a pub Douglas was introduced to Geoff and they got talking. Douglas learned that Geoff's business was in serious trouble. He was going to need to get some big orders soon or the business would go under. Douglas told Geoff of a similar situation in his own life where he had prayed and asked God to help him and God had responded. Would Geoff find it helpful if Douglas was to pray about Geoff's situation? Geoff said that he had no faith in God. Douglas said "Fair enough, but I do have some faith. Could we pray on the basis of my faith?" Geoff felt that there was little to be lost so he let Douglas pray. Douglas did this there and then in the pub. The two met again a week later in the same pub. Geoff had good news – the day after Douglas's prayer he had received the biggest order of his entire life. Some time later Douglas was able to invite Geoff to an outreach event at his church.

Caroline's story

Caroline was our next door neighbour. She was unable to get her son into the school which she felt was essential for his needs. She needed someone to talk to, and she chose us. We listened, and realised that the solution to this situation was out of Caroline's control - but would she like us to pray? We showed her 1 Peter 5.7, which tells us to cast all our anxieties on God. Caroline said, "A bit like putting the problem in his in tray!". "Yes," we said, "exactly like that." We prayed. The next day her son was given a place at the school. The following Sunday the family was to be found in our church.

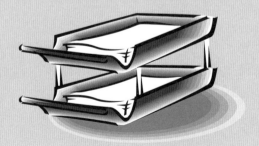